Nita Mehta™
WISKIDZ
ENRICHING YOUNG MINDS

An Imprint of Nita Mehta Publications

MY FIRST BOOK OF
HINDU
GODS & GODDESSES

ANURAG MEHTA

MY FIRST BOOK OF
HINDU
GODS & GODDESSES

Distributed by :
NITA MEHTA BOOKS
3A/3, Asaf Ali Road, New Delhi - 02
Distribution Centre :
D16/1, Okhla Industrial Area, Phase-I,
New Delhi - 110020
Tel.: 26813199, 26813200
E-mail: nitamehta.mehta@gmail.com

Contributing Writers: Editorial & Proofreading:
Subhash Mehta   Rajesh
Tanya Mehta   Ramesh

Editorial and Marketing office
E-159, Greater Kailash II, New Delhi 110 048
Typesetting by National Information
Technology Academy
3A/3, Asaf Ali Road, New Delhi 110 002

Nita Mehta Publications
Enriching Young Minds

Nita Mehta Publications
Corporate Office
3A/3, Asaf Ali Road, New Delhi 110 002
Phone: +91 11 2325 2948, 2325 0091
E-mail: nitamehta@nitamehta.com,
Website: www.nitamehta.com

First Edition 2016

Printed in India at Nova Publications & Printers Pvt. Ltd.

Price: Rs. 125/-   US $ 5.95   UK £ 4.45

CONTENTS

HOW GODDESS SARASWATI WAS CREATED?

Lord Brahma decided to hold a yagna. Now the performing of a yagna had many rules and one of them being that Brahma should sit with his wife, Goddess Savitri, at the prayer fire. Just then, Savitri excused herself and said she would get ready and return to sit with him and perform the prayer. Oh dear, she was taking so long. This angered Lord Brahma. He ordered Lord Indra to find him another wife. Indra quickly found a young cows maid named Gayatri. Brahma immediately blessed her and she became his wife. When Savitri returned and saw what had happened, she was furious.

However, Brahma and the other Gods calmed her. After she calmed down, Savitri merged with Gayatri and helped Brahma in completing the yagna. Thus, the yagna was completed and a new Goddess Saraswati emerged.

WHY AGNI WAS CURSED?

Lord Agni, the god of fire, was to protect the very beautiful wife of the powerful sage Brigu, whilst he was away. Suddenly, the vicious demon, Puloman, appeared. He forced Agni to to tell him the whereabouts of the sage's wife.

The demon did what horrible demons do, he kidnapped her and ran away. Fortunately she managed to escape after some years when Puloman was killed. When she informed Sage Brigu of how Agni had revealed her whereabouts, Brigu was livid. He cursed Agni.

"You shall be an impure eater of all things!" Then Agni applogized and feeling sorry for him, the Sage altered the curse and said that Agni's flames would only consume everything offered to him but his physical body would remain pure.

did you know...

Agni occupies a prominent place in the Vedas and Brahmanas works. The ancient Indians recognized Agni as the power of heat and light and the will-power united with wisdom. They knew the human will-power to be a feeble projection of this power which they believed could be strengthened by the Rig Vedic chants to Agni. There are five kinds of Agni (fire) – Kāla-agni ('the fire of time'), Kśudhā-agni ('the fire of hunger'), Śīta-agni ('the cold fire'), Kopa-agni ('the fire of anger') and Jñāna-agni ('the fire of knowledge').

THE FIRE TEST

Ayodhya, the kingdom of lord Ram was in a celebratory mood. Their king, Ram, his queen Sita and his brother Laxman, who till this point of time were in exile, were returning to the kingdom, after defeating the demon Ravan, who had kidnapped Sita! We all know that every king has his duties that assure his kingdom of his good intentions. Similarly, King Ram was answerable to his people. Here there was a custom to test purity when a terrible instance like kidnapping happened.

Since Sita had been kidnapped by the demon Ravan, she had to prove that she was still pure and untouched by him. The test was a fire test. If Queen Sita was able to withstand the heat of licking flames of a bonfire, she would be deemed pure.

Sita, without a protest, stepped into the bonfire. The flames were burning high. Queen Sita stepped into the fire and sat cross-legged. She closed her eyes and seemed lost in prayer; the dancing flames seemed not to affect her! When the flames died, Sita was unscathed! Every one was overjoyed. She had proved that she was pure and had passed the fire test.

did you know...

Sita is described as the daughter of the earth goddess Bhūmi. According to the Ramayana, Sita was discovered in a furrow when Janaka was ploughing. Since Janaka was a king, it is likely that ploughing was part of a royal ritual to ensure fertility of the land. Sita is considered to be the child of the Mother Earth, produced by the union between the king and the land. Sita is a personification of the Earth's fertility, abundance and well-being.

THE STORY OF NANDI

Nandi, the loyal bull, is Lord Shiva's vehicle. In the incident where the gods & demons churned the oceans for treasures, Nandi came to lord Shiva's rescue in an endearing way. This was when the churning began and the first thing that emerged from the churning was the poison. The poison was so strong that it threatened to destroy the whole world. To protect the world, Lord Shiva, swallowed the poison.

Goddess Parvati who was near Lord Shiva clutched Shiva's throat to make sure that the poison was stored in the throat and would not affect Lord Shiva. However, some poison slipped out and fell on the ground. Nandi gathered the fallen poison and seeing his master drink it, he also drank it! The Devas were amazed at what Nandi had done! But do you know what? Nothing happened to Nandi. He blissfully sat under the ocean absolutely fine. Shiva smiled and declared gratefully, "Nandi is my greatest devotee! All my powers are his too and Parvati's protection will go to him too!"

did you know...

Some Puranas describe Nandi or Nandikeshvara as bull face with a human body that resembles that of Shiva in proportion and aspect, although with four hands — two hands holding the Parasu (the axe) and Mruga (the antelope) and the other two hands joined together in the Anjali (obeisance).

THE WANDERING SAGE

Narad was the wandering sage, who time and again informed one all about impending events. How did he become a wanderer?

The legend says: Lord Brahma ordered King Daksha to create a universe with the help of his family.

King Daksha was married to Asikti. They had five thousand sons. But Narad somehow interfered. He brainwashed the minds of all the sons and they all became saints. That meant they would never marry or have children. This created problem for king Daksha in increasing the population of the universe. After that, Daksha married Panchajani. This time, they had one thousand sons. Again, Narad did the same thing! When King Daksha came to know what was happening, he in fury, cursed, "Narad, You will become an eternal wanderer. You will never remain at a place for long because you have misguided my sons to became wanderers."

did you know...

Narada is a Vedic sage who plays a prominent role in a number of Hindu texts, notably the Ramayana and the Bhagavata Purana. He is well travelled has been to the length and breadth of all cosmic surfaces.

THE PRIZE

Parvati and Shiva were sitting with their sons, one afternoon. Narad came visiting. He carried a gift for them. A magical mango! Shiva handed it to Parvati, his wife, "Here, you eat it first." But Parvati shook her head, "No I cannot eat it without giving it to you and the children first." Narad then intervened saying, "I suggest that you give it to the child who can travel the universe, the quickest! Since it is one mango, let one of them eat it fully!" Everyone agreed. Karthik, the elder son immediately left on his vehicle, the peacock, to circle the universe. But Ganesha, the younger son, just stood and took rounds of his parents three times!

When Karthik returned he saw his parents and Narad standing in awe, staring at Ganesh. "What happened?" asked Karthik.
"Nothing brother, you went around the actual universe three times, but I circled them, our parents, who are the universe for us, three times!" That was true wisdom and so impressed was everyone that Ganesh was given the fruit and many other sweetmeats by his loving mother Parvati, as the rest looked on.

did you know...

The name 'Ganesha' is a Sanskrit compound, joining the words 'gana', meaning a group, multitude, or categorical system and 'isha', meaning lord or master. The word gaṇa when associated with Ganesha is often taken to refer to the 'gaṇas', a troop of semi-divine beings that form part of the retinue of Shiva.

THE THREAT OF THE DEMONESS

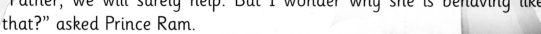

One day, long, long ago, King Dashrath called both the princes, Ram and Laxman, to his chambers. "Sons, I have been asked by Sage Vishwamitra for help. This is for the Sages living in the forest near the river Ganges. They are being harassed by the demoness Taraka."

"Father, we will surely help. But I wonder why she is behaving like that?" asked Prince Ram.

"Rishi Agastya cursed Taraka to lose her beauty and transformed both mother and son into hideous demonic creatures. Taraka along with her son decided to wreak revenge like this!" answered his father.

Both the princes left immediately to help. The Sages were preparing a ritual Yagna fire. As soon as the ceremonies began, there was a loud roar. The sky darkened. Everyone looked up. The demoness Taraka, in a terrible state, began to throw garbage into the scared fire. Lord Ram tried to stop her but her attacks became so ferocious that the saints ran for cover. Lord Ram coming to a decision stood up and with one swift movement, aimed an arrow at her heart. His target hit its mark and Taraka was killed. Peace returned to the forests after that.

did you know...

Rama is the seventh avatar of the Hindu god Vishnu. Rama is also the protagonist of the Hindu epic Ramayana, the story of victory of good over evil.

SHANI & HANUMAN

The forest was deep and dark. There was no sound except that of a low and soft chanting, "Ram, Ram!" The sounds reverberated through the woods. Who was this? It was Hanuman chanting and praying. He was lost in Lord Ram's devotion. Just then, Lord Shani was passing and he noticed Hanuman lost in prayers thus. 'Hmmmm, I have heard Hanuman is powerful and mighty...but I think maybe not as much as me?' Thinking thus, Lord Shani decided to tease Hanuman.

He tried to disturb him but Hanuman was so lost in his prayers that he remained unaffected! Lord Shani then pulled at Hanuman's tail. Whipping in a sudden movement, Hanuman wrapped his tail around Lord Shani in a tight grip.

Lord Shani helplessly struggled to no avail! Then Hanuman finished his prayers and rose in the air to fly home. He forgot that Lord Shani was still wrapped by his tail! Only after he reached home did he realize this. Untangling his tale he apologized to the shaken lord Shani. Shani bowed down and thanked him for releasing him. He also apologized for his teasing and arrogance.

did you know...

The word shani also denotes the seventh day or Saturday in most Indian languages. Hindu traditions often include the worship of Shani with healing rituals that have their origin from local and regional folk traditions.

SHIVA'S TOXIC ENCOUNTER

Related earlier in the book is the story when the gods and demons churned the oceans to release the treasures buried below. Suddenly, a vessel spewing toxic gases abruptly surfaced from the ocean. The gases were so poisonous that the Gods and Demons choked and gasped due to its poisonous nature. This is when Lord Shiva stepped in. He grasped the vapour discharging vessel and drank the contents. Writhing in pain, as the poison seared his throat, Shiva fell down.

Immediately, Goddess Shakti threw a beam, and held the poison in his throat trapping it there. Then, Lord Moon, cast soothing rays to cool off the burns. Shiva's throat turned blue but he not only survived but also helped the continuance of the task of churning uninterrupted thereon.

did you know...

The three coils of the snake around Shiva's neck symbolize the past, present and future - time in cycles. He is also knows as 'Neel Kantha' (blue-throated), for he holds Vasuki's poison in his throat. A third eye on his forehead, shows Shiva as the source of knowledge and wisdom.

A LESSON WELL LEARNT

The entire town of Brindavan was praying to Lord Indra for the bounty of rains he had sent to earth. However, Krishna (who was an incarnation of Lord Vishnu but now on earth in the guise of a cowherd) had different thoughts. "I realize the god of rains and storms is getting a little arrogant. My advice would be to stop praying to him and revert your prays to the Mount Goverdhan instead." He said to the townsmen. Since Krishna was known for giving sound advice, the townsmen listened to him! Oh dear, this made Indra so angry, he furiously unleashed deadly floods and storms on Brindavan.

Krishna immediately collected everyone, Then with super human strength, he lifted mount Goverdhan and used it as an umbrella to protect everyone from the storms! Indra was so shocked at seeing the little cowherd holding up the mountain that he stopped his attack. He became sheepish and realized he had been a wee bit arrogant. He immediately stopped the rains and agreed that he had learnt his lesson.

did you know...

The name Krishna originates from the Sanskrit word 'Kṛṣṇa', which is primarily an adjective meaning 'black', 'dark' or 'dark blue'.The waning moon is called 'Krishna Paksha' in the Vedic tradition, relating to the adjective meaning, 'darkening'.

did you know...

Goddess Kali has 1008 Names that include

1] Smasanakalika : She who is the Remover of Darkness from the Cremation Grounds or from Death

2] Kali : She who is the Remover of Darkness.

3] Bhadrakali : She who is the Excellent Remover of Darkness.

4] Kapalini : She who is the Bearer of the Skulls of Impurity

5] Guhyakali : She who is the Hidden or Secretive Remover of Darkness.

6] MahaKali : She who is the Great Remover of Darkness.

7] Kurukullavirodhini : She who confronts the Forces of Duality.

8] Kalika : She who is the cause of Removing darkness

9] Kalaratrisca : She who is the Dark Night of Egotism

10] Mahakalanitambini : She who is the Eternal Mother of Great Time.

SHIVA FACES KALI'S WRATH

A ferocious battle was on. The nasty and powerful demon Raktabija was locked in a head to head fight with Goddess Kali, who is considered as the Shakti of Lord Shiva.

It seemed like a hopeless war, for Kali at least. Every time she and her warriors cut down Raktabija, wherever his blood fell, another clone of himself appeared. This way, the demons army multiplied. Finally, Kali did not let even one drop of blood fall on the ground. How did she do that? Well, she licked all the falling drops! This way, she singled out the demon and vanquished him. Kali became so heady with this victory that she began the dance of death. She was so blinded that she started killing all she saw. In panic, everyone rushed to Shiva and begged him to help. Shiva knew what to do. He lay down in her path. Totally mesmerized in her own demolition, she did not notice him and stepped on him! It suddenly dawned on her who was lying under her feet. Embarrassed, she thrust out her tongue with shame and moved back. This entire event had a calming effect on her. She abruptly got her wits back. Everyone around breathed a huge sigh of relief!

GANGA COMES TO EARTH

Here we speak of an age where severe penances and deep meditations created magic! In this scenario, we relate the tale of King Sagar who had sixty thousand sons. Oh dear, but unfortunately, they were all killed and their souls were deemed to aimlessly roam the cosmic surfaces. Now the King searched for a solution to release the souls of his sons. There was only one. The pure, river Ganga, who lived in the heavens had to descend to earth where her pure waters would cleanse the souls and release them to go to their heavenly ends.

Ganga, the river, was so strong that if she directed herself towards earth, the earth would split and crumble under her powerful fall! Benevolently, Lord Shiva came forward to help. When Ganga did fall on earth, he trapped her into his locks and released her as seven streams.

Thus, cutting down the burst of powerful weight, which would have damaged the earth surfaces. This way, Ganga came to earth and helped King Sagar.

did you know...

Other names of Ganga: Hara-vallabha (Meaning dear to Hara or Shiva) Himacalendra-tanaya (Meaning daughter of the Lord of Himalayas) Giri-mandala-gamini (Meaning flowing through the mountain country)

Description: In Hinduism, the river Ganges is considered sacred and is personified as a goddess known as Ganga. It is worshipped by Hindus who believe that bathing in the river causes the remission of sins and facilitates Moksha (liberation from the cycle of life and death). The water of Ganga is considered very pure.

HOW BRAHMA GOT FIVE HEADS?

We all know that Brahma is the God of creation. This story relates the time when he had finished the exhausting task of creating the world and everything else in it. When he viewed his Handiwork, he missed something. "I need a companion on my side. I need a wife." Brahma thought. With one magical stroke, he breathed out and "Whoosh!" something emitted from a cloud and stood before him the most beautiful female.

He was so enamoured by her perfect beauty that he just stared at her. She became so shy by his gaze that she began to hide in order to escape it. To catch a glimpse of her, he sprung heads so he could catch a sight of her. Five heads sprung, so he could see behind, sideways and in front! Finally, he proposed marriage to her and she accepted. She is Goddess Saraswati, wife of Brahma, who represents education and learning.

did you know...

The goddess Saraswati is often depicted as a beautiful woman dressed in pure white, often seated on a white lotus, which symbolizes light, knowledge and truth. She not only embodies knowledge but also the experience of the highest reality. Her iconography is typically in white themes from dress to flowers to swan – the colour symbolizing Sattwa Guna or purity, discrimination for true knowledge, insight and wisdom.

did you know...

Names Of Durga: Satī, Sādhvī, the Sanguine; Bhavaprītā, Bhavānī

Description: Durga in Sanskrit means 'the inaccessible' or 'the invincible', is the most popular incarnation of Devi and one of the main forms of the Goddess Shakti in the Hindu pantheon. Durga is the original manifested form of Parvati, Shiva's wife.

Rules over: Fights for good over evil.

THE FURIOUS BATTLE

Once, there lived a terrible demon named Mahishasura. He wreaked havoc on the earthlings and heavenly inhabitants. No one could do anything. But why? The reason being Mahishasura had a boon from Lord Brahma that made him invincible. However, there was one condition. He could only die at the hands of a woman. Lord Brahma and everyone else held a conference to address this horrible problem where their lives were being held ransom by this ruthless demon. Lord Shiva, Vishnu, and Brahma resolutely connected their intense powers, joining a radiance from many powers of all the other gods to create a warrior goddess - Durga. She had a thousand arms. In each arm, she carried a weapon belonging to all Gods. She mounted a fierce lion and challenged Mahishasura. Oh dear, a violent and furious battle ensued. Durga proved to be so strong that Mahishasura had no chance. She chased him to the borders of all realms till she cornered him and slayed him. Peace and calm returned to heavens and earth.

TREASURE OF THE OCEAN

This is a story of the time when the demons and gods actually got together for a common cause. They had to churn the great oceans in order for the ocean to bring out many treasures to the surface. The most precious treasure being the urn of 'amrit' or nectar of immortality. Mount Mandara was used as the churner. Lord Vishnu was the tortoise Kurma on which the Mountain Mandara was balanced. The king of serpents, Vasuki, served as the churning rope. This great exercise went on for many years, with many things going right and wrong! 14 treasures finally surfaced. One of them was Goddess Lakshmi.

She was ordained to be the goddess of prosperity and wealth. As soon as Lord Vishnu saw her, he proposed her to be his wife. She agreed. They lived happily ever after at his abode. Also, whenever Lord Vishnu descends on earth as an avatar, she too accompanies him.

did you know...

Few other names: Rukmini, Kamala, Aditi, Bhaskari, Harini, Mahalakshmi, Narayani, Aishwarya, Roma, Jalaja, Sridevi
Description: Goddess of prosperity.
She gave Indra the drink of soma (wise blood) from her own body so he could produce the illusion of birth-giving and become king of the devas.
Rules over: Wealth, prosperity & success.

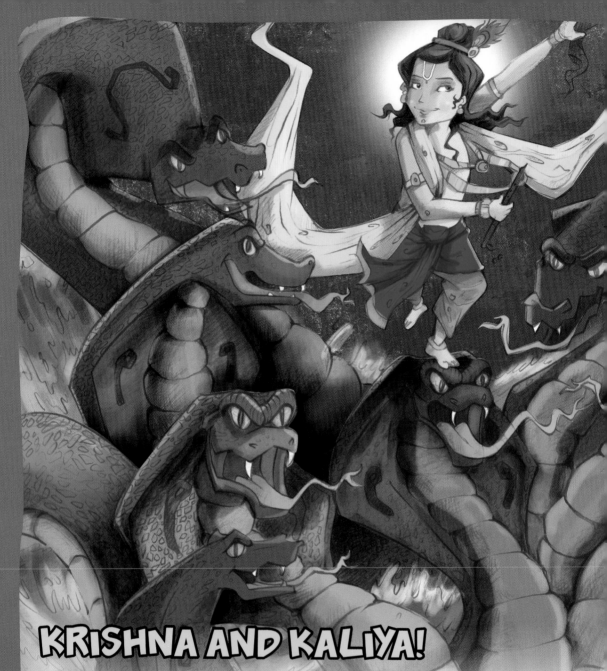

KRISHNA AND KALIYA!

Kaliya Nag was a fierce, hundred hooded serpent, who lived in the river, Yamuna. Oh dear, he spat poisonous gases constantly. This made the waters of the Yamuna so toxic that most fish and other river life died instantly because of it. People found it difficult to live near the river too. It was up to Krishna to fix this problem. One day, he jumped into the river and began to splash noisily.

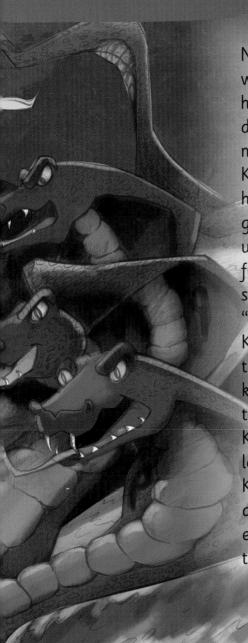

Now that angered Kaliya so much that with a furious snarl, he whipped out his tails and enwrapped Krishna in a death-like lock. Kaliya squeezed ruthlessly, making clear that his intention was to kill Krishna. Suddenly, Krishna began to swell his body. First he doubled, then trebled-growing huge. "Uggggrrrr!" Kallia was unable to hold, let alone squeeze him any further. One point came when Krishna stretched and widened his whole body and "Snapppp," Kaliya released him abruptly. Krishna jumped on Kaliya's hood and began to dance. Kaliya helplessly sank down. He knew that Krishna planned to stamp him to death. Just then Kaliya's wives begged Krishna to spare Kaliya. Krishna agreed to let Kaliya live, but on the condition that Kaliya would go and stay in the far, far away ocean, never to return to the river ever again. Kaliya instantly left much to the joy of the people.

KUBER LEARNS A LESSON

The God of wealth, Kuber, was so proud of his that riches he wanted to boast about it. He made his way to Mount Kailash, the residence of Lord Shiva and his family.

"My Lord Shiva, I am here to invite you for lunch at my home today."

Shiva, who was sitting with his wife Parvati, smilingly shook his head, "I am sorry dear Kuber, but it will not be possible for me to leave Mount Kailash-but here comes Ganesha, our son, take him along."

'Oh my this is luxurious!' Ganesha thought when he saw Kuber's opulent palace! Ganesha narrowed his eyes and watched Kuber arrogantly boasting about his wealth. When Ganesha sat down for lunch, Kuber smirked, "Eat as much as you can Ganesha, in the house of Kuber, there is plenty!" Ganesha began to eat, eat ,and eat! Soon the food in Kuber's entire kingdom finished! But Ganesh a demanded more. He hungrily knocked off pillars and furniture and chewed up everything. When he had finished eating even the jewels in the treasury, he turned and pounced on Kuber, "Aaaaargh I am still hungry- I am going to eat you!" Kuber fled with Ganesha following him. Up the mountains, down the streams, this way, that way, there was no escaping Ganesha! Kuber finally reached Lord Shiva and crumpled at his feet crying, "Lord save me please-Ganesha will eat me!"

Lord Shiva calmly walked up to the cowering Kuber just as Ganesha caught up too. "Here feed him this!" Shiva dropped a handful of rice into Kuber's palm. A trembling Kuber offered the rice to Ganesha. Ganesha ate the rice, burped and smiled—"Hmm now I am full."

Kuber sheepishly apologized to Shiva, "Sorry Lord Shiva-I have learnt my lesson, boasting gets you nowhere...just into a lot of trouble.

did you know...

Few other names: Ganapati, Gajani, Vinayaka, Ekdanta

Description: Elephant-headed god of scribes and merchants. Invoked before starting any work to ensure success.

Rules over: Wisdom, good luck, literature, books, writing, worldly success, prosperity, peace, beginnings, successful enterprises, journeys, building, overcoming obstacles.

HOW HANUMAN FORGOT HIS POWERS?

Did you know that when Hanuman was a child he was so naughty that his mother Anjana was a constant receiver of many complaints. Who complained? The sages who lived in the ashram where Hanuman and his mother lived! Now the sages practiced their Vedic ceremonies and had many rituals to complete. Hanuman was so mischievous that he would run away with their prayer articles. Hanuman was so strong with magical powers that the sages could never catch him. One day, in frustration, they cursed him saying, "You will forget your powers. And only remember them when someone reminds you." Do you know that is exactly what happened. Years later, Hanuman remembered his powers when he joined Lord Ram in his war against Ravan. Hanuman become an ardent devotee of Lord Ram and played an important part in the war between good and evil.

did you know...

Few other names: Sankatmochan, Mahabali, Bajrangbali, Anjanisut, Pawanputra

Description: The son of Vayu and Anjani. Believed to be an avatar of Lord Shiva. The mighty monkey that aided Lord Rama and Laxman in their expedition to find Rama's wife Sita and to end evil forces.

Rules over: Physical strength, courage, bravery, purity, humble and devotion.

KING MANU MEETS LORD VISHNU

One day, King Manu was walking near a pond when a tiny fish called out to him. A talking fish! King Manu was just getting over this amazement when the fish called out again, "Please save me and put me in the river!" King Manu immediately picked up the fish and transferred it to the river. Oh dear, the next day, King Manu visited the river to meet the fish and lo and behold the fish had grown bigger then the river itself! King Manu ordered his men to transfer the fish to the seas. But this fish seemed to be growing really fast. Suddenly it dawned on King Manu that this was not an ordinary fish. Falling to his knees he paid his respects. The fish manifested itself into Lord Vishnu. "King Manu I have a task for you. The floods are coming. It is predicted that the floods will finish the world. I am going to help to save some species to begin a new era. You will build a boat. In that you will take seven sages, seeds of every plant, a pair of each animal and birds. I will appear as a fish and drag the boat up to Mount Himavan. This way humans and species will survive the floods."

King Manu immediately built a boat as ordered by Lord Vishnu. Lord Vasuki, the serpent of the waters helped Lord Vishnu, in his Matsaya Avatar, transformed as a fish, pull the boat over the waters up to Mount Himavan. Once safely atop, the inhabitants in the boat, watched the floods wreak havoc over the lands. Finally, the floods receded. They then safely descended from the mountain and walked forth to begin a new era.

did you know...

Lord Vishnu has come to earth nine times. His nine incarnations are also seen as stages of evolution for mankind. His various forms or *Avatars* were: **Matsaya** (fish), **Kurma** (tortoise), **Varaha** (boar), **Narasimha** (man-lion), **Vamana** (dwarf), **Parashurama** (a powerful warrior), **Ram**, **Krishna**, **Buddha**. Predictions say that his tenth *Avatar* **Kalki** (machine-man) will come at the end of the present age (**Kaliyuga**). Kalki will come riding a white horse.

BRAHMA LOSES HIS FIFTH HEAD

"I am superior!" claimed Lord Vishnu calmly to Lord Brahma, who snapped back, "No, I am superior!" Lord Shiva appeared and decided to settle the argument. "I will create a pillar of light. Whoever, between the two of you, finds the end or start of this column of light will be deemed superior!"

Lord Vishnu immediately turned into a boar and burrowed downwards. Lord Brahma turned into a swan and flew upwards. Oh dear, the column was endless and both the Gods could not find the end or start. Lord Vishnu gave up and returned. Lord Brahma, however, on his way up, caught hold of a flower called Ketaki who happened to be floating down. He decided to lie. On his return, he said, "I found the top of the column of light and here is a flower, which was resting atop."

Lord Shiva was enraged. He knew Lord Brahma was lying. What angered him even more was that the flower too lied along with Brahma.

Lord Shiva's anger transformed him into another form; that of demon Bhairav. With one slice of a chopper, Bhairav chopped off Lord Brahma's fifth head. He cursed Ketaki to lose all her loveliness and said that it would never be offered as a flower to the gods.

did you know...

Do you know why Brahma **wears off-white clothes?** Since pure white means purity, his off white clothes represents the acceptance of opposites in existence.

For Example: purity and impurity, happiness and unhappiness, vice and virtue, knowledge and ignorance.

If you observe the image of Brahma, he holds beads or a rosary in his back right hand. Now what does this rosary signify? The rosary denotes the time cycle through which the world moves from creation to maintenance, from sustenance in to dissolution, and from dissolution to new creation.

THE CURSE OF THE MOON

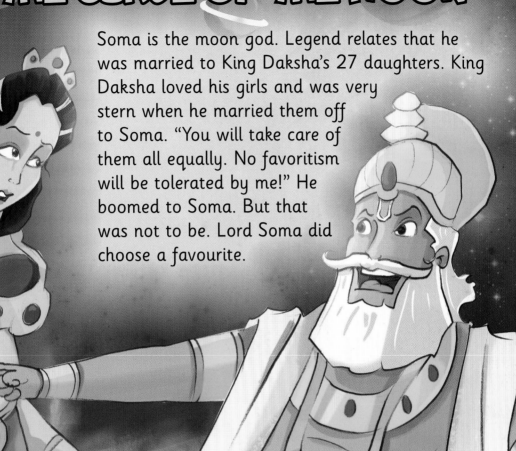

Soma is the moon god. Legend relates that he was married to King Daksha's 27 daughters. King Daksha loved his girls and was very stern when he married them off to Soma. "You will take care of them all equally. No favoritism will be tolerated by me!" He boomed to Soma. But that was not to be. Lord Soma did choose a favourite.

Princess Rohini! Now this fact was related to King Daksha who was furious! King Daksha lost his temper. He lifted a finger and pointing at Soma, cursed him to a slow, painful death. But his daughters were frightened and they begged their father to reconsider. Calming down, Daksha changed his curse, "You will not be seen always .You shall wax and wane in the sky. This way, you will constantly remember your mistake."Thereon the Moon was destined to be seen in different stages of vison, sometimes full, sometimes quarter or sometimes just visible! This explains the Moon's periodic appearances.

WHEN YAMA WAS TRICKED

Yama is the god of death. Once, Yama came to earth and married a mortal woman. They even had a son. He was named Yama Kumar. Unfortunately, Yama and his wife never got along. In disgust, Yama returned to his heavenly kingdom. From there, he proudly saw his son become a doctor. "Son, my advice to you is to treat only those patients who are going to the live. If you see me standing near any patient, be assured that the patient, is untreatable and is going to die." Yama Kumar agreed. Once the Princess of the realm fell very ill. Horrified, Yama Kumar saw his father at her bedside. After a few days, Yama Kumar had an idea on how to save the princess!

Yama Kumar in a loud voice, exclaimed, "Greetings Mother! Good you are here ! Father will be here soon!" Now this was all a pretense! He was fooling his father. Yama stopped short. His wife was here? With a snort, he turned heels and ran all the way back to his kingdom. He did not want to meet his wife ever, you see! Yama Kumar giggled and was grateful that Yama forgot the princess in his rush to run away from his wife! He knew his father would not return soon. So the princess lived on.

did you know...

In Vedic tradition, Yama was considered to have been the first mortal who died and went to heaven. In some passages, however, he is already regarded as the god of death.

Other titles available...

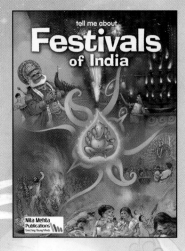

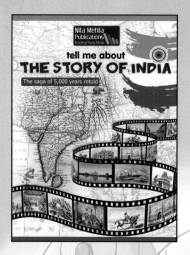

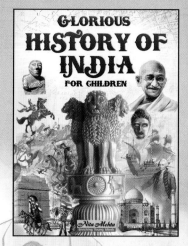

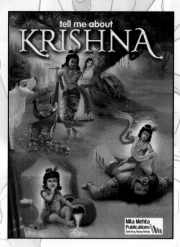

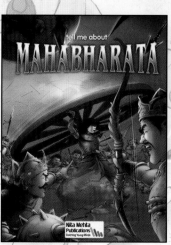

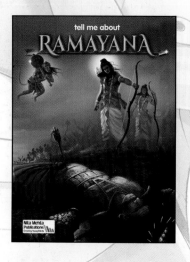

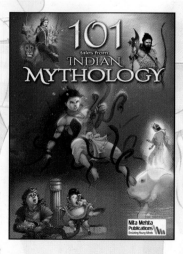

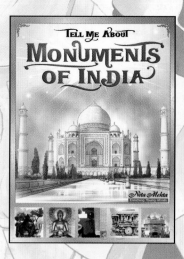